S0-BBN-150

Applying Problem-Solving Strategies

5–6

Written by

Angela Higgs

Editor: Heather Butler
Illustrator: Corbin Hillam
Production: Karen Nguyen
Cover Designer: Barbara Peterson
Art Director: Moonhee Pak
Project Manager: Collene Dobelmann
Project Director: Betsy Morris

© 2007 Creative Teaching Press Inc., Huntington Beach, CA 92649
Reproduction of activities in any manner for use in the classroom and not for commercial sale is permissible.
Reproduction of these materials for an entire school or for a school system is strictly prohibited.

Table of Contents

Introduction

Applying Problem-Solving Strategies 5–6 contains dozens of ready-to-use activity pages to provide students with skill practice. The fun activities can be used to supplement and enhance what you are already teaching in your classroom. Give an activity page to students as independent class work, or send the pages home as homework to reinforce skills taught in class. An answer key is provided at the end of the book for quick reference.

This book provides activities that will directly assist students in practicing strategies needed to solve word problems. The activities are grouped in three-page sets that cover each problem-solving strategy. The first activity page of each set includes the subhead "Show Me the Way" because it demonstrates step-by-step for the student how to use the strategy. The remaining pages offer students a chance to practice using the strategy to solve similar problems. Please note that the problems in each section could be solved using multiple strategies.

Use these ready-to-go activities to "recharge" skill review and give students the power to succeed!

Name _____ Date _____

Page Puzzle

SHOW ME THE WAY TO WORK BACKWARDS

Mrs. Ballard told her students she had a puzzle for them to solve. She told them that she was thinking about two pages in their science book whose page numbers add up to 49. The pages were facing each other in the book. Which pages was Mrs. Ballard talking about?   _____

Strategic Steps

1 If the pages face each other, what does that tell you about the page numbers? If you are not sure, open any book and see the page numbers.

2 Since you know the sum of the two numbers, working backwards will help solve this problem. Subtract 1 from 49 to make the number even for Step 3.

49 – 1 = _____

3 Take the answer from Step 2 and divide it by 2.

_____ ÷ 2 = _____

4 The answer is the left-facing page number. Add this to the page number that would come next and see if they equal 49.

_____ + _____ = 49

Applying Problem-Solving Strategies • 5–6 © 2007 Creative Teaching Press

On Time

A Melissa wants to go to a movie that starts at 7:25 p.m. Before the movie, she has to clear the table and load the dishwasher, which takes 13 minutes; do her math homework for a quarter of an hour; and do her nightly reading, which will take her three times as long as her math homework. It should take her 12 minutes to get to the theater and find a seat. What time does she have to start her chores and homework to be in her seat 5 minutes before the movie starts?

B Saturday morning, Eden has a soccer game that starts at 8:30 a.m. It takes her a third of an hour to get ready, 4 minutes to make her bed, 13 minutes to eat breakfast, and 18 minutes to ride her bicycle to the soccer field. If she has to be to the field 25 minutes before the game starts, what time does she have to get up?

C Hunter had several chores to do before he could go swimming with his friend at 11:20 a.m. Unloading the dishwasher and putting away the dishes takes 12 minutes. Cleaning his room takes twice as long. Then he needs 20 minutes to pick up the sticks in the front yard so his dad can mow the lawn. It takes 34 minutes to walk to his friend's house, but instead he's going to save 20 minutes by riding his bike. What time does Hunter need to start his chores?

Applying Problem-Solving Strategies • 5–6 © 2007 Creative Teaching Press

Going Backwards

A Janessa rode her bicycle from school to the library, from the library to the park, and then home. She rode a total of 9.7 miles, and it is 3.3 miles from the library to the park and 2.6 miles from the park to her house. The next day she took the same route but did not stop at the library. How far is it from the school to the park?

B Jase made brownie bites to share with his friends. He saved three to give to his brother, and passed around the rest of the brownie bites. Jim took a half dozen, Brynn took a third as many brownie bites as Jim, Rissa took two and a half times more than Brynn, and there were three brownie bites left for Jase. How many brownie bites did Jase make?

C Kim had a lot of party favors left over from her party. She gave Bree half of them. Bree gave Surri half of hers. Surri gave two to each of her three sisters and kept the remaining four for herself. How many party favors did Kim have before she gave some to Bree?

D Mr. Butler had a puzzle for his class to solve. He asked the students to turn to the facing pages in their textbook that add up to 629. What pages are those?

Applying Problem-Solving Strategies • 5–6 © 2007 Creative Teaching Press

Name _____ Date _____

Ping-Pong Tournament
SHOW ME THE WAY TO SOLVE A SIMPLER PROBLEM

There are 8 players in a Ping-Pong tournament. Each of these players must play each other. How many games will be played? _____

Strategic Steps

1 For this problem, break it into several easier steps. Assign each of the 8 players a letter to make it easier, such as A, B, C, D, E, F, G, and H. Start with player A and pair that player with the seven other players.

Player **A**: A vs. _____ A vs. _____ A vs. _____ A vs. _____ A vs. _____

A vs. _____ A vs. _____

2 Move on to each player and continue listing all the new games each player will play. Remember not to list the same game twice. For example, A vs. B and B vs. A is the same game and should not be repeated.

Player **B**: B vs. _____ B vs. _____ B vs. _____ B vs. _____ B vs. _____ B vs. _____

Player **C**: C vs. _____ C vs. _____ C vs. _____ C vs. _____ C vs. _____

Player **D**: D vs. _____ D vs. _____ D vs. _____ D vs. _____

Player **E**: E vs. _____ E vs. _____ E vs. _____

Player **F**: F vs. _____ F vs. _____

Player **G**: G vs. _____

Player **H**: no new games

3 Once you have finished, count the number of games to get the total played during the tournament.

Applying Problem-Solving Strategies • 5–6 © 2007 Creative Teaching Press

Ice Cream!

After their soccer tournament, some teams went to an ice cream stand. The flavors were strawberry cheesecake, mango, cherry, mixed berry, coconut, hazelnut chocolate, pistachio, mint chip, chocolate, and peanut butter. The stand had a special in which you could get two scoops for the price of one. Each kid got the special with two different flavors. Between all of them, every combination was chosen and nobody had the same combination. Find all the different combinations of flavors to find the number of kids.

How many kids were there? _____

Strawberry
cheesecake:_____

Mango:_____

Cherry:_____

Mixed berry:_____

Coconut:_____

Hazelnut
chocolate:_____

Pistachio:_____

Mint chip:_____

Chocolate:_____

Peanut butter:_____

Applying Problem-Solving Strategies • 5–6 © 2007 Creative Teaching Press

Name _____ Date _____

Game Time

Mrs. Miller's class has an ongoing checkers tournament three times a week after school. There will be 14 students playing in the tournament. Each of these students will be paired with the others to play a game. The games will continue until every student has played each of the other 13 students. How many games will be played in the tournament?

_____

Player **A**: _____

Player **B**: _____

Player **C**: _____

Player **D**: _____

Player **E**: _____

Player **F**: _____

Player **G**: _____ Player **H**: _____

Player **I**: _____ Player **J**: _____

Player **K**: _____ Player **L**: _____

Player **M**: _____ Player **N**: _____

Aquarium

Show Me the Way to Solve Multiple-Step Problems

Max and Jenna are helping find the things they need for the new 90-gallon aquarium that will be in their school.

A The aquarium needs one pound of gravel for each gallon of water. If the gravel is sold in 5-pound bags and there are 4 bags to a case, how many cases of gravel do they need to buy?

_____

Strategic Steps

1. To find out how many pounds of gravel there are in a case, multiply the weight of each bag by how many bags are in a case.   5 pounds per bag × 4 bags per case = _____ pounds per case

2. Find out how many cases are needed by dividing the total pounds of gravel needed by the number of pounds in a case. If the quotient has a remainder, an extra case must be purchased.   90 pounds ÷ _____ pounds per case = _____ cases

B Max and Jenna have decided to buy 38 fish. Max picked out 9 guppies and Jenna chose twice as many mollies. They also want to buy some tetras. How many tetras can they buy? _____

Strategic Steps

1. Find out how many mollies Jenna would like to buy. She chose twice as many as Max picked out, so multiply how many guppies Max chose by 2.   9 × 2 = _____ mollies

2. Now add that number to the guppies.   _____ guppies + _____ mollies = _____ fish

3. To find out how many tetras they can buy, take the sum from Step 2 and subtract that from the total number of fish they plan to purchase. 38 – _____ = _____ tetras

Applying Problem-Solving Strategies • 5–6 © 2007 Creative Teaching Press

Baked Goods

A Brennen can make 6 cakes in 2 days. How many cakes can he make in 5 days?

_____

B Allison needs 1 ½ cups of flour to make a batch of her cookies. If a pound of flour has 4 cups and flour is sold in 4-pound bags, how many batches of cookies can she make from one bag of flour?

_____

C Kyle's dad is having a barbecue. Kyle went to the bakery for him. His dad needs 10 hamburger buns, 14 hot dog buns, and 15 onion rolls. He can buy the following items in packs for the price listed, but he decides to buy the buns and rolls individually for the same price so that he does not have any leftovers:

Bakery Sale

Hot Dog Buns	—	6 for $2.10
Hamburger Buns	—	6 for $2.94
Onion Rolls	—	6 for $3.30

How much will it cost? _____

Name _____ Date _____

Art Class

A Mrs. Bitner's art class is preparing for an art show. She needs to make sure she has enough paintbrushes and canvas frames. There are 48 students who want to make paintings for the art show. Canvases are only sold in packs of 4 and paintbrushes in packages of 6. How many packs of each will she need?

B Jeanne needs 5 pounds of clay to make 3 vases. How many vases can she make with 20 pounds of clay?

C Emily is going to build a model house with craft sticks. For each of the four sides, she will need 76 sticks. For the roof she will need half as many craft sticks as she used for all of the sides together. How many craft sticks will she need in all?

D Catt and Zoe went to New York City with their dad to see some of the art they had learned about in art class. They planned to walk from their hotel to an art museum, but their dad said they didn't have time to walk the 25 blocks. He told them that every block was ⅕ of a mile. They took a taxi instead. While they rode, the girls tried to figure out how much the taxi fare would be. The rates were posted in the taxi: initial fee—$2.50, every ⅕ mile—40¢, and every minute idle—20¢. The girls calculated the fare without including the minutes idle, or waiting. What did they think the cab fare would be?

Applying Problem-Solving Strategies • 5–6 © 2007 Creative Teaching Press

Name _____   Date _____

Museum Trip

SHOW ME THE WAY TO EXCLUDE EXTRA INFORMATION

Ms. Andrew's class is going to the museum. There are 29 students in the class. Five parents are going as chaperones. Mrs. Chong's class is on the same bus with 22 students and 6 parents. Half of Mr. Gomez's class is also on that bus. He has 26 students and 8 parents. At the museum, they will meet up with Mr. Adams's class of 24 students and 4 parents and Mrs. Schneider's class with 21 students and 5 parents.

How many students are on the bus with Ms. Andrew and Mrs. Chong? _____

Strategic Steps

1 Some of the information is not needed to solve the problem. Look to see what the problem is asking you. Do you need to know how many parent chaperones went with each class? Were all the students on the bus with Ms. Andrew and Mrs. Chong?

2 Cross out the information that is not needed. Add together the number of students that were on the bus with Ms. Andrew and Mrs. Chong. Remember to divide the number of students in Mr. Gomez's class in half.

_____ + _____ + _____ = _____

Applying Problem-Solving Strategies • 5–6 © 2007 Creative Teaching Press

Name _____ Date _____

Beach Walk

A Mr. Fulton's class went to the beach to collect shells. This beach was fun because of all the types of shells. Mike found 4 oyster shells and 2 clam shells. Arley found 2 conch shells. Kathryn found 12 scallop shells and 6 jingle shells. Bryan found 2 clam shells. Kathryn found 9 jingle shells. How many shells were clams?

B After collecting shells, the class ate their sack lunches on the beach. Four kids had peanut butter and grape jelly on wheat bread, and three had it on white bread. Two kids had ham on rye, and six kids had peanut butter and honey on white bread. Of the five kids that had peanut butter and raspberry jam on wheat bread, two of them traded their sandwiches for shells. Seven kids forgot their lunches and three kids did not have sandwiches so they bought fish tacos. How many sandwiches had peanut butter on them?

C Mr. Fulton asked the class to help pick up trash along the beach. Their goal was to recycle at least 20 pounds of trash. The students picked up 10 pounds of cans, 8 pounds of plastic, 5 pounds of paper waste, and 6 pounds of nonrecyclable items. How many pounds of waste did they recycle?

Applying Problem-Solving Strategies • 5–6 © 2007 Creative Teaching Press

Name _____   Date _____

Skiing Time

A Maria's family went on a cross-country ski trip. They drove 156 miles to get to the first ski trail. The first day they skied 25 miles. The next morning they skied 8 miles. Then they drove 38 miles to the second ski trail. There they skied 12 miles. The next day they drove 50 miles to another ski area with 2 trails. The first trail was 6 miles and the second was 7 miles. Then they drove 122 miles home. How many miles did Maria's family drive?

B On their trip, Maria's family stayed at a different place each night. The first place was a cabin that cost $99. Their meals at the cabin totaled $86, but they had a voucher that saved them $20. The second night they stayed at a ski lodge for $129. Maria's mom bought a scarf at the gift shop for $11.99. The last night, Maria's family stayed at their neighbor's time-share so they got 40 percent off the rate of $150. Before they went home, they went on a sleigh ride that cost $20 for their family. How much did Maria's family spend on lodging?

C Maria's family decided that the kids could each spend $20.00 on the trip. Mark purchased a T-shirt that was 20 percent off and spent $16.82, Maria spent $7.99 on a ski charm for her bracelet, and Nick spent $17.99 on a new ski mask. Each family member was under the budget by at least $2.00. How much did the kids spend altogether?

D Each night, Maria's family watched the news to see the weather report for their next day of skiing. Before they left, the weather report said the first day's high would be 36 degrees with a 30 percent chance of snow. The next night's report said the actual high was 35 degrees. The forecast called for a mostly sunny day with a high of 39 degrees. At the second ski trail, the warmest reading on Maria's jacket thermometer was 40 degrees. That night they watched the weather report and saw that a cold front was moving in. Their final destination was supposed to have a high of 29 degrees. The high ended up being 30 degrees. What was the actual average high temperature during their ski trip?

Applying Problem-Solving Strategies • 5–6 © 2007 Creative Teaching Press

Name _____ Date _____

Batter Up!

Show Me the Way to Use Data from a Chart

The following chart shows the stats from a 12-game season of the local White Sox Little League baseball team.

Team Members	Hits	Singles	Doubles	Triples	Home Runs
Melissa	10	5	1	3	1
Christopher	15	6	4	5	0
Liz	18	11	2	4	1
Sammie	23	12	1	9	1
Katie	8	1	0	6	1
Nick	11	2	1	6	2
Ron	15	6	3	6	0
David	11	2	0	8	1
Jeff	9	2	5	1	1
Kayla	18	8	2	4	4

A How many total hits did the White Sox have this season? _____

Strategic Step

1. Add all the numbers in the "Hits" column to find the total.

B How many more singles were there than doubles? _____

Strategic Step

1. Add all the numbers in the "Singles" column, and then do the same for the "Doubles" column. Subtract the total from the "Doubles" column from the "Singles" column total.

C What fraction of Kayla's hits were home runs? _____

Strategic Step

1. Take the number of home runs for Kayla and make that the numerator. The number of hits becomes the denominator. If needed, reduce the fraction to its lowest terms.

Applying Problem-Solving Strategies • 5–6 © 2007 Creative Teaching Press

Name _____ Date _____

How Many Pages?

The students in one of Mr. Devin's reading groups made a chart to keep track of the number of pages they read each week during a reading contest. Use this chart to answer the questions below.

Students	Week 1	Week 2	Week 3	Week 4
Kimberly	208	196	315	155
Pam	178	156	112	186
Savanna	312	78	56	35
Doug	98	135	173	672
Gerald	315	275	346	24
Jayson	102	114	99	121

A Find the students who had the greatest and fewest total number of pages read. How many more pages did the one student read than the other?

B What is the average number of pages read by the six children during week 2?

C How many more pages did Doug read than Gerald altogether?

D In which weeks did two students each read greater than 300 pages?

Applying Problem-Solving Strategies • 5–6 © 2007 Creative Teaching Press

Collections

The fifth grade took a survey to see how many students had collections. They entered the data in the following chart.

Class	Trading Cards	Stuffed Animals	Stamps	State Quarters
Mrs. Estrada's	14	9	4	2
Mr. Swift's	12	18	0	1
Mrs. Matthews's	16	3	2	4
Ms. Demarco's	18	6	1	2

A In Mrs. Estrada's class, how many more stuffed animal, stamp, and state quarter collections combined were there than trading card collections?

B Which class had the greatest total number of collections?

C In Ms. Demarco's class, what fraction of the collections were stuffed animals?

D Mrs. Matthews's class had the greatest number of _____ collections.

Applying Problem-Solving Strategies • 5–6 © 2007 Creative Teaching Press

Name _____   Date _____

Birthday Fun

Show Me the Way to Guess and Check

For Zane's eleventh birthday, he went with his parents and three younger brothers to a sporting event. The total cost for the tickets was $64.00.

Which sporting event did the family attend? _____

Baseball:	Adult $9.00	Child (under 12) $5.00
Soccer:	Adult $13.50	Child (under 12) $10.00
Tennis:	Adult $15.00	Child (under 12) $8.50

Strategic Steps

1 Since this is a Guess and Check strategy, choose the sporting event that you think could be the correct answer. You know that there are two adult tickets and four child tickets. The first guess could be baseball. Calculate the cost of baseball tickets for the family. Multiply the adult ticket price by 2, multiply the child ticket price by 4, and then add the two answers together.

$(\$9.00 \times 2) + (\$5.00 \times 4) =$ _____

2 The cost of those tickets do not equal $64, so use the same steps to price the soccer and tennis tickets for the family to find the correct answer.

Applying Problem-Solving Strategies • 5–6 © 2007 Creative Teaching Press

Make Your Best Guess

A Shelby and Kate were counting the drawings in their art portfolio. Shelby had 6 more drawings than Kate. Altogether, they had 34 drawings. How many drawings does each girl have?

B Tom and Gordon collect rocks. Tom has 32 more rocks than Gordon. Altogether, they have 158 rocks. How many rocks does each boy own?

C Amanda went to the book sale. She bought two books and paid with a $10 bill. One book was a dollar more than the other and she got back $1.02 as change. How much did each book cost?

D Miranda and Becca ran in a race. Becca finished 5 minutes after Miranda. Altogether, their times added up to 59 minutes. What was each girl's finish time?

Applying Problem-Solving Strategies • 5–6 © 2007 Creative Teaching Press

Name _____   Date _____

Time and Measurement

A Xavier and Aaron compared their heights. If you add their heights together, they are 9 feet 4 inches tall. Xavier is 4 inches taller than Aaron. How tall is each boy?

B Brinley and Neha had a contest to see who could climb the climbing wall at the school the fastest. They took turns and timed each other with a stopwatch. Neha's time was 2 seconds more than Brinley's time. If you add the girls' times together, you get 19 seconds. How long did it take each girl to climb the wall?

C Tyler and Ed were throwing a Frisbee. Tyler threw the Frisbee 9 feet farther than Ed. Altogether, they threw the Frisbee 61 feet. How far did each boy throw the Frisbee?

D Belle and Michael were seeing who could jump rope the most times at recess. Belle jumped 23 more times than Michael. Altogether, they jumped 105 times. How many times did each child jump?

Applying Problem-Solving Strategies • 5–6 © 2007 Creative Teaching Press

Rodeo Function

SHOW ME THE WAY TO USE FUNCTIONS

Today was the annual City Rodeo. Xavier and Clay helped set things up and arrived early to make sure everything was perfect. They were surprised to see that all the numbers and times posted on the sign had been changed. The cost for rodeo tickets had been changed from $5 to $9. The time for the first event had been changed from 10 a.m. to 19 a.m. (Who has ever heard of 19 a.m.?) The only number that was unchanged was the calf-roping event scheduled for 1 p.m.

Taped to the entry gate was a note that said, "I love functions! My job is to change numbers. If you can't find out what I am, I will keep changing numbers." It was signed, The Function Master. While Clay was reading the note, Xavier saw the following on the back of the note: "Here are my favorite functions: $F = n + 4$ $F = 2n + 1$ $F = 2n - 1$ and $F = 4n - 5$.

Which one did I use?" _____

Strategic Steps

1 A function is a pattern of numbers that are changed in the same way. In the formulas, F is the number after it has been changed and n is the number that will be changed.

2 Look at the numbers that have been changed and find a pattern. Use the first function ($F = n + 4$) to see if it works? For the cost of the rodeo tickets, F would be 9 and n would be 5. Does $9 = 5 + 4$?

_____

3 If the function works using 9 and 5, try the second set of numbers—10 turning into 19—to see if it also works. If not, go on and try the next function until you find the one where both sets of numbers work. Once they do, see if the number 1 remains unchanged in this function, then you have the answer.

Applying Problem-Solving Strategies • 5–6 © 2007 Creative Teaching Press

Name _____ Date _____

The Visitor

Donavan came home and found the Function Master sitting in his living room. The Function Master had changed some numbers and would continue changing numbers until Donavan told him the function being used. The Function Master said he only changes one digit in each number at a time. For example, if the number was 43, first he would change the 4, then the 3.

Donavan's address is 34 S. 72nd St., but the Function Master changed it so that it reads 24 S. 100th St. When Donavan tried to call his friend Jesse, and he dialed a 5, it became a 6. The number 7 became 10. Only the number 4 stayed the same.

The Function Master gave Donavan a list of his favorite functions:

$F = 2n + 1$

$F = 3n + 6$

$F = 2n - 6$

$F = 2n - 4$

Which function did the Function Master use? _____

Applying Problem-Solving Strategies • 5–6 © 2007 Creative Teaching Press

Homework Headache

Mateo was helping his little sister with her math homework. They left the paper on the table while they got a snack. When they came back, all the numbers had been changed and the answers were wrong! There was a note attached to the homework paper saying, "I couldn't help myself, I had to change the numbers. To get your work back, you must discover the function I used." The note was signed, the Function Master.

The number sentence $2 + 3 = 5$ had become $1 + 3 = 7$, which isn't even correct! The number sentence $3 + 4 = 7$ had become $3 + 5 = 11$. Every number except the number 3 has changed. Mateo saw that there was scribbling on the back of the note and found the following functions:

$F = 2n + 1$

$F = 3n + 6$

$F = 2n - 3$

$F = 2n - 4$

Which function did the Function Master use? _____

Applying Problem-Solving Strategies • 5–6 © 2007 Creative Teaching Press

Name _____ Date _____

Garden Club

SHOW ME THE WAY TO MAKE A CHART

Maya, Livia, and Celine planted a flower garden at the school. On Monday, they each planted two flowers. Every day, each girl planted one less than two times as many flowers as she did the day before. How many flowers did the girls plant during the week?

_____

Strategic Steps

1 Find the number of flowers planted on Monday by multiplying the number of girls by how many flowers they each planted. Write the answer on the chart.

Day	Flowers Planted
Monday	flowers
Tuesday	flowers
Wednesday	flowers
Thursday	flowers
Friday	flowers

2 Find out how many flowers were planted by one girl on Tuesday. $(2 \times 2) - 1 =$ _____

3 Multiply the answer from Step 2 by 3 to get the total for the girls.

_____ $\times 3 =$ _____ flowers planted on Tuesday

4 To find out how many flowers were planted by one girl on Wednesday, take the answer from Step 2 and find one less than two times that number.
$(3 \times 2) - 1 =$ _____

5 Multiply that answer by 3 to get the total for the girls.

_____ $\times 3 =$ _____ flowers planted on Wednesday

6 Continue working until the chart is filled in. To find the number of flowers the girls planted for the week, add the numbers in the "Flowers Planted" column.

Applying Problem-Solving Strategies • 5–6 © 2007 Creative Teaching Press

Allowance

Brady's dad told him that he could choose which way he could get his allowance. With Option A, he would receive $15 each month. With Option B, Brady would get $0.63 in January, and the amount would double each month after that. Make a chart showing how much he would receive each month with both options. Calculate the total with each option.

Which is the better long-term option for Brady to take? Explain.

_____

_____

_____

Month	Option A	Option B
January		
February		
March		
April		
May		
June		
July		
August		
September		
October		
November		
December		
Total		

Applying Problem-Solving Strategies • 5–6 © 2007 Creative Teaching Press

Name _____ Date _____

Ecology Club

The Ecology Club at school is using river rocks to build a path through the school garden. On Monday, Mrs. Broadman said she had started the path with 10 rocks the day before. She said that the students needed to double the number of rocks put in place each day in order to finish the path by Friday. Each student could only put 5 rocks in the path. Make a chart that shows the number of rocks placed in the path each day and how many students worked that day.

Day	Number of Rocks Placed	Number of Students
Sunday	10	0

Applying Problem-Solving Strategies • 5–6 © 2007 Creative Teaching Press

Name _____ Date _____

Roller Coaster

Show Me the Way to Draw a Picture

Ann, Alex, Maria, Nick, and Shea were in line to ride a roller coaster. Use the following clues to make a picture showing the order in which they were standing:

- Alex is first in line.
- Ann is fourth in line.
- Maria is between Ann and Alex.
- Ann is in front of Shea.
- Nick is in front of Maria.

Strategic Steps

1 According to the first clue, label the first person as Alex.

2 The second clue says that Ann is fourth in line. Label the fourth person Ann.

3 The fourth clue says that Ann is in front of Shea, so label where Shea must be in line.

4 That leaves the third and fifth clues to locate where Maria and Nick are standing. Label them.

Applying Problem-Solving Strategies • 5–6 © 2007 Creative Teaching Press

Name _____ Date _____

Summer Job

Jan spent her summer working for her dad in his office building. One day the elevator was out of service, so she had to take the stairs to deliver packages to offices on different floors. When she was finished, she met her dad for a smoothie at the building's café and realized that she was halfway between the top and bottom floors.

Use the following clues to find out how many floors her dad's building has:
- She started at her dad's office on the bottom floor.
- Her first delivery was ten floors up.
- Then she went down three floors to pick up a package.
- She ran off some copies the next floor down.
- Next, she took a break and walked down the hall to the café and got a smoothie.

How many floors are in her dad's office building?

_____

Applying Problem-Solving Strategies • 5–6 © 2007 Creative Teaching Press

Name _____ Date _____

Oral Reports

Five students in Mrs. Nielson's class are presenting their oral reports in front of the class. Mrs. Nielson said they would go in order from youngest to oldest.

Use the following clues to find the order the students will present their reports:
- Bethany is older than Cassidy.
- Mallory is older than Bethany.
- Tye is younger than Bethany.
- Cassidy is older than Tye.
- Ethan is older than Bethany but younger than Mallory.

What order did the children present their reports?

_____

_____

Applying Problem-Solving Strategies • 5–6 © 2007 Creative Teaching Press

The Park

SHOW ME THE WAY TO SOLVE MULTIPLE-ANSWER PROBLEMS

At the park, Devin was lying on the grass watching people walk their dogs across a bridge. He counted 16 legs. Fill in the chart to find all the possible combinations of dogs and people that could have been in that group.

Strategic Steps

1 There is more than one possible answer to this problem. Organize the information into a chart to see which combinations equal 16.

People	Legs	Dogs	Legs	Total Legs	Does It Work?
$1 \times 2 =$	2	$2 \times 4 =$	8	$2 + 8 = 10$	No
$2 \times 2 =$	4	$3 \times 4 =$	12	$4 + 12 = 16$	Yes

2 So far one answer works. See if you can find other answers that work.

Applying Problem-Solving Strategies • 5–6 © 2007 Creative Teaching Press

Food Storage

Vicki's mom bought 60 pounds of flour for their food storage. The flour was sold in 5- or 10-pound bags. Fill in the chart to identify the combinations of each sized bag she could have purchased.

5-Pound Bags	10-Pound Bags	Total Pounds	Does It Work?

Applying Problem-Solving Strategies • 5–6 © 2007 Creative Teaching Press

Insects and Spiders

Roy and Brent each made a display of insects and spiders. In Roy's display box there were 44 legs. In Brent's box there were 52 legs. Fill in the chart to find all the possible combinations of insects and spiders in each boy's box.

Insects	Legs	Spiders	Legs	Total Legs	Does It Work?
____ × 6 =	_____	____ × 8 =	_____	___ + ___ =	

Applying Problem-Solving Strategies • 5–6 © 2007 Creative Teaching Press

Name _____ Date _____

Close Enough

Show Me The Way To Estimate

Sometimes you need an exact answer to a problem and sometimes you just need to be close to the answer. Read each of these problems and decide if you need an estimate or an exact answer.

A Shane has to drop off a package at the post office, and then he will meet his friends at the park to play basketball. He leaves home about 3:30 p.m. He thinks it will take 13 minutes to get to the post office and drop off the package. Then it will take him another 8 minutes to get to the park. About what time should his friends expect him? _____

Strategic Steps

	Actual Time	Time rounded
		(to the nearest 5-minute interval)

1. The keyword *about* is used, which means that it is all right if the answer is off by a few minutes, so an estimate is fine. Round the times to the nearest 5-minute interval.

13 minutes   _____

8 minutes   _____

2. Add these times to 3:30 p.m. to get the estimated time that Shane will arrive at the basketball court.

3:30 p.m. + _____ = _____ p.m.

B You and your friend played a computer game and compared points. If you had 23,374 points and your friend had 22,298, how many more points did you have than your friend? _____

Strategic Steps

1. Since the problem does not use the keyword *about*, an exact answer must be found instead of an estimated amount.

2. Subtract the smaller number from the larger to get an exact answer.

_____ – _____ = _____

Applying Problem-Solving Strategies • 5–6 © 2007 Creative Teaching Press

Name _____   Date _____

What Time?

A After school, Alicia needs to finish her project, go to band practice, and then talk to the teacher. Band practice usually takes 37 minutes. She thinks it will take 22 minutes to finish her project and about 17 minutes to talk to her teacher. If school is over at 3:00 p.m., about what time should she tell her mother she will be leaving school?

B Carla has three errands to run before meeting her friend Amy for lunch. Carla arrives to the Town Center Mall at 10:30 a.m. to run all of her errands. She will probably be at the craft store for 12 minutes, the post office for 8 minutes, and then the library for about 24 minutes. From there, it will take about 4 minutes to arrive at Burger Shack. About what time should she tell Amy to meet her at Burger Shack?

C On Alicia's way home from school, she stopped at the music store to buy music books. She found four books she wanted, but could only buy two. The prices were $22.39, $14.89, $17.99, and $21.69. If she only had $36.00, which two books did Alicia buy?

D For lunch, Carla ordered a salad that cost $5.99. Amy's pizza cost $7.99. Both girls ordered sodas for $1.80 each. How much did their lunch cost altogether?

Applying Problem-Solving Strategies • 5–6 © 2007 Creative Teaching Press

Name _____ Date _____

Cross Country

A Walter's family is moving from Philadelphia, PA, to Sacramento, CA. Along the way, Walter wants to stop at Mount Rushmore near Keystone, SD. His sister wants to stop at the Rock and Roll Hall of Fame in Cleveland, OH. Their parents said that they would visit the place that adds the fewest miles to their trip. Walter used the Internet to find the following distances.

Starting City	Ending City	Mileage
Philadelphia	Keystone	1,694
Keystone	Sacramento	1,295
Philadelphia	Cleveland	432
Cleveland	Sacramento	2,380

Which place will Walter's family visit on their cross-country trip? _____

B Edmund and Alonzo were discussing the lengths of two long hiking trails, the Pacific Crest Trail along the West Coast and the Appalachian Trail along the East Coast. The Pacific Crest Trail is 2,655 miles long. The Appalachian Trail is 2,161 miles long. If you round to the nearest hundred, approximately how much longer is the Pacific Crest Trail?

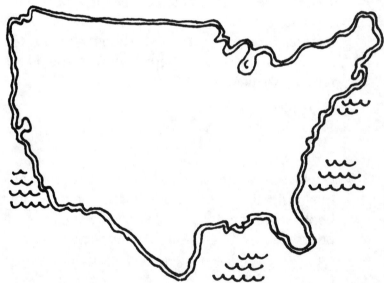

C The tallest mountain peak in North America is Mt. McKinley. It is 20,320 feet above sea level. The tallest mountain peak on earth is Mt. Everest, located in Asia. It stands 29,035 feet above sea level. What is the approximate difference between their heights if you round to the nearest thousand?

Applying Problem-Solving Strategies • 5–6 © 2007 Creative Teaching Press

Name _____ Date _____

Going to School

Ruthann walks 1.25 miles to school every day. How many miles to and from school does she walk in a week?

Strategic Steps

1 This problem is asking for assumed information. This means that some information needed to solve it is not stated in the problem. The problem assumes that you already know that students go to school five days a week. Also, it is assumed that if she walks to school, she will also walk home. That doubles the distance.

2 Now that the assumed steps have been found, solve the problem. First, find out how many miles Ruthann walks roundtrip for school in one day by multiplying the distance by 2.

$1.25 \times 2 =$ _____ miles walked in a day

3 To find how many miles she walks to travel to and from school in a week, multiply the answer from Step 2 by 5.

_____ $\times 5 =$ _____ miles walked in a week

Applying Problem-Solving Strategies • 5–6 © 2007 Creative Teaching Press

Name _____ Date _____

Water, Water, Everywhere

A Megan's mother is trying to drink 64 ounces of water a day. How much water will Megan's mother drink in a week?

B Megan's mother only drank 58 ounces of water per day. At that rate, how much water will she drink in July?

C Jessica needs 6 ounces of water for every 2 ounces of fruit juice for her punch recipe. If she makes one quart of punch, how much water will she use?

D Jessica made punch for a birthday party. She needed at least ten 8-ounce servings. If she makes 2 quarts, will she have enough punch? Explain.

Applying Problem-Solving Strategies • 5–6 © 2007 Creative Teaching Press

Name _____ Date _____

Go the Distance

A Christine is practicing for her school's cross-country track team. Every day she runs 12 laps on the school track. How many laps did she run in October if the only days she took off were her birthday on the 12th and Halloween?

B Alyssa rides her bicycle every day. The trail she rides is 6.5 miles to the end. If she rides to the end and back on the same trail every day, how many miles will she ride in a week?

C How many miles will Alyssa ride if she rides the same trail every day in February during leap year?

D Danika entered her homemade go-cart in a 5-mile race. After speeding along for 10,560 feet, one of the wheels started to come loose. She repaired the wheel as fast as she could. How many more miles did Danika have to go to finish the race?

Applying Problem-Solving Strategies • 5–6 © 2007 Creative Teaching Press

Name _____ Date _____

Sleepover

Show Me the Way to Use Venn Diagrams

The 15 girls from Mr. Tate's class are having a sleepover. Six girls are wearing
slippers, five girls are wearing socks, and two girls are wearing both.
The rest of the girls have bare feet. How many of the girls have bare feet? _____

Strategic Steps

1 Use a Venn diagram to organize the data. At the top corner of the box containing the Venn
diagram, write the total number of girls at the sleepover. Then label one circle *Slippers* and the
other circle *Socks*. The overlapping section is for girls who are wearing both slippers and socks.

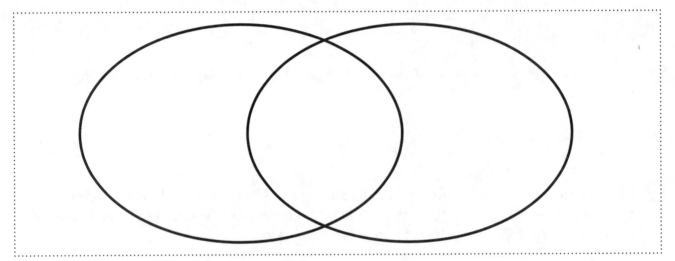

2 Start in the overlapping section and draw two tally marks representing the number of girls
wearing slippers and socks.

3 Next, add tally marks in the slippers-only section so that the number of tallies in the slippers-
only section and the slippers and socks section totals six.

4 Then add tally marks to the socks-only section. Remember
to only add enough tally marks so that the socks-only
section and the slippers and socks section total five.

5 Total the tally marks and subtract that answer from
15 to find out how many girls are in bare feet.

15 – _____ = _____

Applying Problem-Solving Strategies • 5–6 © 2007 Creative Teaching Press

Team Events

Name _____ Date _____

A There are 27 children on the swim team. In a competition, 11 of the children swam the breast-stroke and 12 swam the backstroke. Nine of those children swam both the breaststroke and the backstroke and the rest swam the butterfly. How many children swam the butterfly?

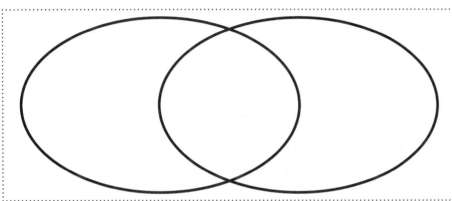

_____

B There are 87 students participating at a regional track meet. Of that total, 45 ran the 100-meter dash, 38 ran the 200-meter dash, and 15 of those ran both. The other students participated in other events. How many students participated in other events?

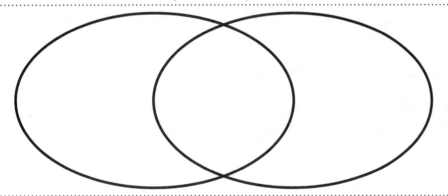

_____

C The track meet was attended by 150 spectators. Of the spectators, 47 rooted for athletes from Jackson Middle School and 63 supported participants from Butler Middle School. There were 20 people who rooted for both of those schools. How many spectators were there to support other schools?

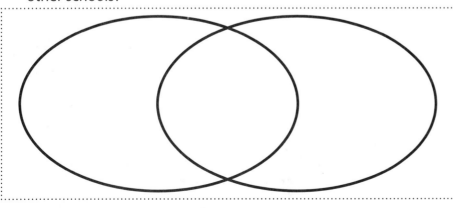

_____

Applying Problem-Solving Strategies • 5–6 © 2007 Creative Teaching Press

Use Venn Diagrams **41**

Name _____ Date _____

Student Surveys

A Ruth surveyed some fifth graders to find out who preferred to watch television or play video games. She found that 21 liked to watch television, 18 liked to play video games, and 13 of those students liked both. The remaining 4 students said they liked neither.

How many students did she survey? _____

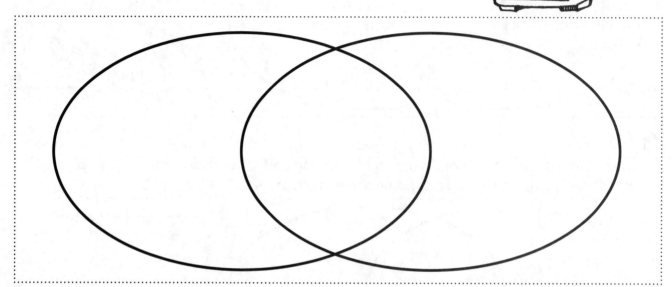

B At an assembly, Dan counted students wearing either blue or green, or both colors. He counted 26 wearing blue and 35 wearing green. Of those students, 17 were wearing both green and blue.

How many students did he count altogether? _____

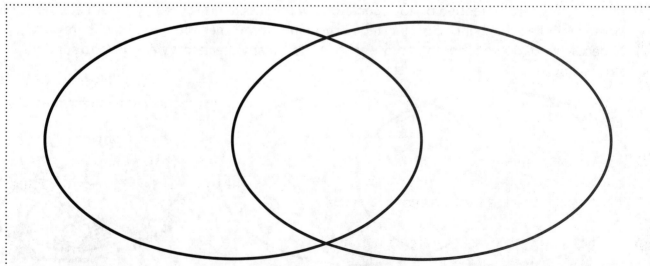

Applying Problem-Solving Strategies • 5–6 © 2007 Creative Teaching Press

Fun Run

SHOW ME THE WAY TO USE LOGIC SQUARES

Hillary, Jana, Mason, and Max were the first four to finish the sixth grade's 5K race. Each wore a jersey during the race with the numbers 2, 4, 7, or 12 on it.

Use the following clues to find which number each student wore:
- Max wore a number that was smaller than Mason's.
- The student wearing number 7 said her knee hurt.
- The father of number 12 took his son out for ice cream afterwards.
- Jana wore an even number.
- Max's number was the same as his finishing order.
- Max finished last in this group.

	2	4	7	12
Hillary				
Jana				
Mason				
Max				

Strategic Steps

1 The first clue tells us that Max can't have the biggest number and Mason can't have the smallest number. Mark X under the biggest number in Max's row and the smallest number in Mason's row to eliminate that choice.

2 The second clue uses the pronoun *her*. Mark X under *7* on Mason's and Max's rows.

3 The third clue refers to the student as someone's son. Mark X under *12* on the girls' rows. This leaves Mason as number 12, so mark Y for *yes* for Mason. Likewise, mark X in the remaining box in Mason's row.

4 The next clue eliminates the odd number for Jana. Mark X in Jana's row in the box under the odd number. The only spot left in this column is in Hillary's row, so mark Y in that box. Mark X in the box for each of the other numbers for Hillary.

5 The fifth and sixth clues tell us Max's number. Mark this on the grid. That leaves only one option for Jana.

Applying Problem-Solving Strategies • 5–6 © 2007 Creative Teaching Press

Name _____ Date _____

Countries

Ana, Justine, Masa, and Tanner have all lived in other countries. These countries are Germany, Brazil, Australia, and France.

Use the following clues to match each child with the country in which he or she lived:
- Ana and Tanner have the same number of letters in their countries' names.
- Masa lived in a country with an "e" in its name.
- Ana lived below the equator.

	Germany	Brazil	Australia	France
Ana				
Justine				
Masa				
Tanner				

Applying Problem-Solving Strategies • 5–6 © 2007 Creative Teaching Press

Name _____ Date _____

Favorite Fruit

Andrew, Jane, Clark, and Kendra love fruit. Each has a favorite fruit that is either apples, oranges, strawberries, or kiwi.

Use the clues to match each child with his or her favorite fruit:
- Neither of the girls likes apples.
- The girl with the shortest name doesn't like oranges.
- The color of Jane's favorite fruit is also her favorite color.
- Only one child's favorite fruit starts with the same letter as his or her name.
- Jane wore her favorite color for picture day—scarlet.
- Kendra does not like kiwi.

	Apples	Oranges	Strawberries	Kiwi
Andrew				
Jane				
Clark				
Kendra				

Applying Problem-Solving Strategies • 5–6 © 2007 Creative Teaching Press

Answer Key

Page Puzzle (page 4)

pages 24 and 25

On Time (page 5)

A. 5:55 p.m.

B. 7:10 a.m.

C. 10:10 a.m.

Going Backwards (page 6)

A. 7.1 miles

B. 19 brownie bites

C. 40 party favors

D. pages 314 and 315

Ping-Pong Tournament (page 7)

28 games

Ice Cream! (page 8)

45 kids

Game Time (page 9)

91 games

Aquarium (page 10)

A. 5 cases

B. 11 tetras

Baked Goods (page 11)

A. 15 cakes

B. 10 batches

C. $18.05

Art Class (page 12)

A. 12 packs of canvas, 8 packs of brushes

B. 12 vases

C. 456 craft sticks

D. $12.50

Museum Trip (page 13)

64 students

Beach Walk (page 14)

A. 4 shells

B. 18 sandwiches

C. 23 pounds

Skiing Time (page 15)

A. 366 miles

B. $318.00

C. $42.80

D. 35 degrees

Batter Up! (page 16)

A. 138 hits

B. 36

C. 2/9

How Many Pages? (page 17)

A. 642 pages

B. 159 pages

C. 118 pages

D. weeks 1 and 3

Collections (page 18)

A. 1

B. Mr. Swift's

C. 6/27 reduced to 2/9

D. Trading Card

Birthday Fun (page 19)

Tennis

Make Your Best Guess (page 20)

A. Shelby — 20 drawings
Kate — 14 drawings

B. Tom — 95 rocks
Gordon — 63 rocks

C. $4.99 and $3.99

D. Becca — 32 minutes
Miranda — 27 minutes

Time and Measurement (page 21)

A. Xavier — 4 feet, 10 inches
Aaron — 4 feet, 6 inches

B. Brinley — 8.5 seconds
Neha — 10.5 seconds

C. Tyler — 35 feet
Ed — 26 feet

D. Belle — 64 jumps
Michael — 41 jumps

Rodeo Function (page 22)

$F = 2n - 1$

The Visitor (page 23)

$F = 2n - 4$

Homework Headache (page 24)

$F = 2n - 3$

Garden Club (page 25)

Day	Flowers Planted
Monday	6
Tuesday	9
Wednesday	15
Thursday	27
Friday	51
Total	108 flowers

Allowance (page 26)

Month	Option A	Option B
January	$15.00	$0.63
February	$15.00	$1.26
March	$15.00	$2.52
April	$15.00	$5.04
May	$15.00	$10.08
June	$15.00	$20.16
July	$15.00	$40.32
August	$15.00	$80.64
September	$15.00	$161.28
October	$15.00	$322.56
November	$15.00	$645.12
December	$15.00	$1,290.24
Total	$180.00	$2,579.85

Answers will vary. Answers should be similar to: Option B will give Brady much more by the end of the year.

Ecology Club (page 27)

Day	Rocks	Students
Sunday	10	0
Monday	20	4
Tuesday	40	8
Wednesday	80	16
Thursday	160	32
Friday	320	64

Roller Coaster (page 28)

Alex

Nick

Maria

Ann

Shea

Summer Job (page 29)

13 floors

Oral Reports (page 30)

Tye

Cassidy

Bethany

Ethan

Mallory

The Park (page 31)

People	Dogs
2	3
4	2
6	1

Food Storage (page 32)

5-Pound Bags	10-Pound Bags
12	0
10	1
8	2
6	3
4	4
2	5
0	6

Insects and Spiders (page 33)

Roy — 6 insects and 1 spider or 2 insects and 4 spiders

Brent — 6 insects and 2 spiders or 2 insects and 5 spiders

Close Enough (page 34)

A. about 3:55 p.m.

B. 1,076 points

What Time? (page 35)

A. about 4:20 p.m.

B. about 11:20 a.m.

C. She bought the books priced at $14.89 and $17.99.

D. Their lunch cost $17.58.

Cross Country (Page 36)

A. the Rock and Roll Hall of Fame in Cleveland, OH

B. about 500 miles

C. about 9,000 feet

Going to School (page 37)

12.5 miles

Water, Water, Everywhere (page 38)

A. 448 ounces

B. 1,798 ounces

C. 24 ounces

D. No. She needs 80 ounces, and 2 quarts is only 64 ounces.

Go the Distance (page 39)

A. 348 laps

B. 91 miles

C. 377 miles

D. 3 miles

Sleepover (page 40)

6 girls

Team Events (page 41)

A. 13 children

B. 19 students

C. 60 spectators

Student Surveys (page 42)

A. 30 students

B. 44 students

Fun Run (page 43)

Hillary — 7

Jana — 2

Mason — 12

Max — 4

Countries (page 44)

Ana — Brazil

Justine — Australia

Masa — Germany

Tanner — France

Favorite Fruit (page 45)

Andrew — apples

Jane — strawberries

Clark — kiwi

Kendra — oranges